FRIENDLY FRANCO
by TONY GARTH

Franco was a very friendly little boy. He wanted to be friends with everyone. And everyone wanted to be friends with him!

One day, a new boy started at Franco's school. He was put in Franco's class. Franco knew that his name was Antonio, and that he seemed very shy.

"I'll make friends with him," thought Franco. "It'll make him feel more at home."

So, at break time, Franco went to find Antonio. He was standing all on his own.

"Hello," Franco said. "I'm Franco, and I'd like to be your friend."

Antonio looked puzzled. "Qué?" he said. Then he walked away.

Franco was hurt that Antonio didn't seem to want to be his friend. Later on, he offered Antonio one of his sweets. Antonio took the sweet but he still looked puzzled.

"Qué?" he said, again. "Amigo?"

Franco shook his head. "They're sweets," he said. "Not amigos."

"No amigo?" Antonio asked.

"No," said Franco.

Antonio looked sad, and walked away.

When it came to games, Franco asked Antonio if he'd like to be on his team. Everyone wanted to be on Franco's team!

"Si! Bueno. Gracias," said Antonio.

But nobody knew what he meant.

After lunch, Franco decided to have one more try at making friends with Antonio.

"Would you like to be my friend?" he asked.

Antonio looked surprised. "Amigo?" he said, hopefully.

Franco shook his head. "No," he said. "Friend!"

"No amigo?" said Antonio. Franco shook his head.

Once again, Antonio looked sad and walked away.

At dinner time, Franco was very quiet and thoughtful. "What's the matter?" asked his Mum.

"Antonio doesn't want to be my friend," replied Franco, glumly. "And I don't know why."

"I'm sure he does want to be friends," said his Dad. "It must be strange for him being so far from home and in a different country. Give him time and I'm sure you'll be best friends."

"He keeps saying funny things like amigo," said Franco.

His Mum and Dad laughed. "Well, there you are," said his Mum. "Antonio does want to be friends after all."

"What do you mean?" asked Franco.

"Amigo means friend in Spanish," said his Dad.

Franco was very relieved.

"Nobody told me Antonio was Spanish!" he said. "When I asked him to be in my team for games, he said gracias, or something like that. What does that mean?"

"That means thank you in Spanish," said his Mum.

Franco's Dad taught him some useful Spanish words. There was Hola! which means hello, and bienvenido! which means welcome.

Next morning, Franco was really looking forward to going to school and to seeing Antonio again.

Antonio was standing on his own in the playground. Franco went up to him.

"Hola!" he said and pointed at himself. "Yo me llamo Franco. My name is Franco."

Antonio smiled. "Yo me llamo Antonio," he said, pointing at himself.

"Bienvenido! Welcome to my school!" said Franco.

"Muchas gracias," said Antonio.

"Thank you," said Franco.

"Thank you," said Antonio.

From that moment on, Franco and Antonio became the best of friends.

Franco helped Antonio to learn English. Antonio taught Franco Spanish. And they remained amigos forever!

Collect all 30 titles in the Little Monsters series